ELEVATING YOUR KID'S GROWTH

By Kerry Galarza and Steve Ritter

For bulk orders, please call 630.832.6155 or email booksales@teamclock.com

Published by Center for Team Excellence.

ISBN: 978-0-9890132-6-0
www.CenterforTeamExellence.com

Printed In The United States of America.

Table of Contents

FAMILY ENVIRONMENTAL ASSESSMENT TOOL

By identifying key environmental influences in development and tracking subtle changes in real time, families can strengthen each cycle of their child's developmental progress, thus maximizing growth, learning and adaptation.

Who will benefit from the Family Environmental Assessment Tool (FEAT)?

The FEAT is designed to measure environmental factors for children and adolescents of all ages and levels of functioning. It is designed for children with identified needs, children with suspected needs, children who are managing adequately in most settings but may be having some difficulty at home or in other surroundings, and children who are doing well but might benefit from a check-in.

What does the FEAT measure?

The FEAT is a simple, organized method to weigh environmental influences on growth in real time. Perhaps even more useful, it can reveal how each environmental influence fluctuates throughout the cycles of a child's growth.

Foundation, connection, growth and resilience are the four pillars of the FEAT. Within these domains, there are eight core criteria: medical & clinical history, family expectations, family dynamics, caregiver needs, developmental stage, enablers & obstacles, support systems and

child/adolescent readiness.

Each of the criterion are easily measured on a 5-point scale from delayed to advanced, depending on the unique circumstances of the child and family. The information provided by the scale can then be used to guide the priorities of intervention or adapt the child's environment if intervention is not recommended.

In addition, pre/post measurements enable progress to be tracked. Environmental factors ebb and flow in impact over time. Comparing measurements at regular intervals ensures that growth interactions are tailored toward and remain matched to the child and their family as time goes on.

By measuring and tracking regularly, subtle factors are added to the plan in a timely manner to address the child's unique path. Helping professionals, educators, parents and caregivers can stay informed about the child's growth opportunities with ongoing and real-time assessment and reassessment.

Where & when should I administer the FEAT?

The FEAT can be completed by parents/caregivers, helping professionals or a partnership between them. Because there are no additional materials necessary, it is easily administered in clinics, schools, daycares or home settings.

There is no prescribed setting or timeline for this to occur. It can be used by parents or caregivers at any point when some insight or guidance is desired. Within therapeutic relationships, it can be used at the time of intake or evaluation, and at any time thereafter.

In a standard therapeutic assessment timeline, a child's performance is revisited at milestones or when pronounced changes have occurred. Typically, revision to the treatment plan might happen only once a year, which can miss smaller shifts in a child's environment. The FEAT is specially designed to capture these transitions.

Aspects of the environment may be stable for a while followed by rapid changes. Failing to pay attention to small changes limits the potential for growth. Allowing for regular monitoring of subtle changes leads to much more tailored and effective interactions.

The FEAT is designed to provide a simple, straightforward way to discover how environmental factors are impacting growth at any point in time.

Why should I add the FEAT to my toolbox?

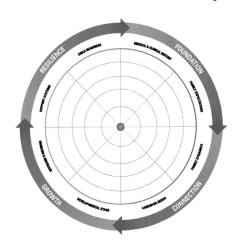

While most assessments chart linear growth, development tends to occur in cycles. Each cycle forms a new *foundation* of strengths, enables the ability to *connect*, feeds *growth* and empowers *resilience which, in turn, strengthens the foundation.*

These four key drivers have ebbs and flows that define a child's unique developmental course. This process happens visibly in the first few decades and then at a more subtle pace throughout the lifespan.

Environment and growth are always connected. By determining how the domains in the cycle operate together, changes can be regularly tracked. Armed with that data, interactions can be customized to suit a child's current and future circumstances.

Most developmental assessments for children also tend to focus on problem identification. Their purpose is to target and measure individual skill areas. However, this method typically doesn't provide much, if any, information about the impact of the child's environment.

This matters because every interaction that promotes growth is fed by social, emotional and physical factors. Some are obvious (distracting noises, shared pleasure), but many aren't (anxiety, fatigue). Environmental influences that fly under our radar can leave important gaps.

Continuous review of past, current and imminent influences on a child and family is the key to helping kids grow.

Why care so much about the environment?

The environment shapes learning. This becomes clear to everyone if and when a child begins to receive intervention and relationships develop. Tweaks can then be made as intervention unfolds, but too much is left up to chance when it's done without intention.

Everyone's behavior results from interactions between internal states and changing physical, emotional and social environments. This starts simply in the womb, when a developing fetus is shaped by prenatal conditions. Once the baby is born, the environment immediately takes on infinite new facets. With the first breath, the child's experience of the environment begins influencing the way he or she behaves, thinks, connects, grows and processes experiences.

All people experience lifelong change, yet transitions during childhood tend to be more pronounced as internal development is still ma-

turing. Even when all seems calm to an onlooker, the child's brain is in a busy state of learning and adjustment. Growth is a result of this continuous internal response to external factors.

A healthy environment boosts growth and development. Even in the best conditions, kids' environments are always shifting. These changes are natural fuel for growth in every person's life. Unless environmental influences are identified and factored in, the full potential of any interaction is lessened.

Why focus so much on the family?

The family shapes the foundation and the framework of a child's environment. Family members function as primary gatekeepers, architects, administrators and teachers in their child's world. Unfortunately, family needs, desires and influences are often left out of initial planning when only traditional skills-based assessments are used. Understanding the family unit is central to designing successful intervention for children.

A family's routines also play into an intervention's ultimate success. For instance, if a caregiver is preoccupied by other demands, they can't be fully engaged. If unaware of learning goals, they are less likely to help teach skills. If a family doesn't have access to safe playgrounds, then peer interaction and play must happen differently. Getting a clear picture of these elements, and countless others, steers recommendations for learning.

How do I administer the FEAT?

Begin by using the Domain Assessment Criteria sheets provided. Review each Domain Description and Domain Goal, considering the ways in which each specific domain may pertain to the child and family.

FAMILY

ENVIRONMENTAL

ASSESSMENT

Score your child/family along the 5-point scale based upon the depiction under each rating within the Assessment Criteria Chart. (1: Delayed, 2: Lagging, 3: In-Progress, 4: On-task, 5: Advanced.)

You may use the space provided to mark each rated domain under the "PRE-" and "POST-" columns, or simply circle the appropriate rating on the Assessment Criteria Chart.

After all eight Domain Assessment Criteria are assigned a rating, fill in the circumplex by shading in the corresponding number within each pie wedge. Each segment of a wedge correlates with the number score.

For example, a score of "1" is illustrated by shading the segment closest to the center of the circle, while a score of "5" is illustrated by shading in all segments of the wedge.

Once completed, the circumplex allows a quick, impactful way to view growth and cyclical change from one assessment period to the next. By comparing two (or more) of them side by side, you can easily see where the child and family are functioning within the pillars of *foundation, connection, growth and resilience*. This then allows you a platform from which to create or modify interventions in order to harness your child and family's strengths and elevate deficiencies.

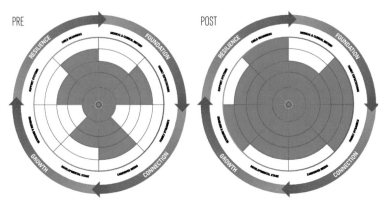

TOOL

An additional note:

The administration of the FEAT may prompt sensitive conversations. In fact, that is what it is meant to do. Without these conversations, parents and caregivers may not be aware of how some of their unique family environmental factors are contributing to their child's development. In all probability, the more sensitive the conversation, the more likely it is to be impacting growth.

Environmental factors are notable in their ability to shape-shift, blend, and even hide in plain sight. This workbook simply provides a way to highlight the subtle influences contributing to growth and development so we can help kids learn in the best manner possible.

FAMILY

ENVIRONMENTAL

ASSESSMENT

TOOL

Family Environmental Assessment Tool™ Methodology Overview

1. Examples of "delayed," "lagging," "in progress," "on task" and "advanced" are defined for each domain (1/2/3/4/5).
2. Scores in each domain are plotted on the circumplex for a visual representation of the child's current state.
3. Intervention plans are created to harness strengths and elevate deficiencies.
4. Pre/post assessment tracks progress and recalibrates goals as the child's environmental circumstances evolve.

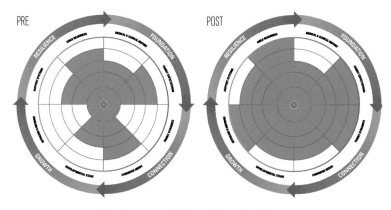

Intervention Strategies

FOUNDATION

Medical & clinical history _____
Family expectations _____

CONNECTION

Caregiver needs _____
Family dynamics _____

GROWTH

Developmental stage _____
Environmental congruence _____

RESILIENCE

Access to resources _____
Child/adolescent disposition _____

FAMILY

ENVIRONMENTAL

ASSESSMENT

TOOL

10

Family Environmental Assessment Tool™
Domain Assessment Criteria

Medical & Clinical History

Domain description:

Medical and clinical history inform current planning and approach to intervention:

- Time elapsed since first concern.
- Past and current clinical partnerships.
- Past and current treatment outcomes.
- Corroboration of past and current diagnoses, if any.

Domain goal: Complete medical and clinical history is incorporated within the intervention plan.

Assessment Rating

Pre	Post
☐ Delayed	☐ Delayed
☐ Lagging	☐ Lagging
☐ In-progress	☐ In-progress
☐ On-task	☐ On-task
☐ Advanced	☐ Advanced

Assessment Criteria

1	2	3	4	5
Delayed	Lagging	In-progress	On-task	Advanced
Intervention planning and/or execution is mismatched with the child's needs based on medical and clinical history.	Intervention planning and/or execution is occurring in the absence of complete medical and clinical information.	Complete medical and clinical information has been obtained and is under review.	Comprehensive medical and clinical history, including all past and current clinical partnerships, is included in the scope of intervention.	Past and current medical and clinical partnerships are included in the scope of intervention, and regular collaboration is occurring between team members.

11

Family Expectations

Domain description:

Family/caregiver concerns and expectations inform current planning and approach to intervention:

- Goals and priorities.
- Previous experience and existing knowledge base.

Domain goal: Family and caregiver(s) concerns and expectations have been identified and are central to the intervention plan.

Assessment Rating

Pre	Post
☐ Delayed	☐ Delayed
☐ Lagging	☐ Lagging
☐ In-progress	☐ In-progress
☐ On-task	☐ On-task
☐ Advanced	☐ Advanced

Assessment Criteria

1	2	3	4	5
Delayed	Lagging	In-progress	On-task	Advanced
Intervention planning and/or execution is mismatched with family/caregiver concerns or expectations.	Intervention planning and/or execution is occurring without incorporation of family/caregiver concerns or expectations.	Family/caregiver concerns and expectations are actively being investigated and taken into consideration for intervention planning.	Some family/caregiver concerns and expectations have been included in the scope of intervention.	Family/caregiver concerns and expectations are central to intervention planning and execution.

Family Environmental Assessment Tool™
Domain Assessment Criteria

Family Dynamics

Domain description:

Consideration of the impact of intervention on the family's relationships, routines and style of interaction based upon:

- Relationship wellness between child & caregiver and between collaborating caregivers.
- Family structure.
- Each family member's priorities and needs.
- Individual and family schedule.

Domain goal: Intervention is tailored to promote the family's unique circumstances as correlated with relationships, routines, and interactions.

Assessment Rating

Pre	Post
☐ Delayed	☐ Delayed
☐ Lagging	☐ Lagging
☐ In-progress	☐ In-progress
☐ On-task	☐ On-task
☐ Advanced	☐ Advanced

Assessment Criteria

1	2	3	4	5
Delayed	Lagging	In-progress	On-task	Advanced
Intervention is negatively impacting family routines and relationships.	Intervention is occurring without consideration for family routines and relationships.	Intervention is occurring with some consideration for broader family routines and relationships.	Intervention is actively incorporating family routines and relationships.	Intervention is occurring in a manner that supports and promotes optimal family routines and relationships.

FAMILY

ENVIRONMENTAL

ASSESSMENT

Family Environmental Assessment Tool™
Domain Assessment Criteria

Caregiver Needs

Domain description:

Caregiver needs inform current planning and approach to intervention:

- Emotional/psychological/physical requirements.
- Levels of support.
- Recurring responsibilities.

Domain goal: Caregiver needs have been identified and are incorporated into the intervention plan.

Assessment Rating

Pre	Post
☐ Delayed	☐ Delayed
☐ Lagging	☐ Lagging
☐ In-progress	☐ In-progress
☐ On-task	☐ On-task
☐ Advanced	☐ Advanced

Assessment Criteria

1	2	3	4	5
Delayed	Lagging	In-progress	On-task	Advanced
Caregiver is struggling with the management of recurring responsibilities and/or unmet emotional, psychological or physical needs.	Intervention planning and/or execution is occurring without regard for or incorporation of caregiver needs.	Caregiver needs are actively being investigated and taken into consideration for planning but have not yet been fully integrated into intervention.	Caregiver needs have been included in the scope of intervention and implemented where easiest access is possible.	Caregiver needs are understood and fully incorporated into intervention planning and execution.

TOOL

Family Environmental Assessment Tool™
Domain Assessment Criteria

Developmental Stage

Domain description:

Identification of the child/adolescent's broad-spectrum developmental stage as it pertains to intervention planning and participation, within the following areas of development:

- Cognitive
- Physical
- Communication
- Sensory Integration
- Social-Emotional
- Adaptive

Domain goal: Child/Adolescent's broad-spectrum developmental stage and its impact on the scope of the primary concern guides the creation/execution of the intervention plan.

Assessment Rating

Pre	Post
☐ Delayed	☐ Delayed
☐ Lagging	☐ Lagging
☐ In-progress	☐ In-progress
☐ On-task	☐ On-task
☐ Advanced	☐ Advanced

Assessment Criteria

1	2	3	4	5
Delayed	Lagging	In-progress	On-task	Advanced
Intervention planning and/ or execution is mismatched with the child's developmental stage.	Intervention planning and/ or execution is occurring without guidance of child/ adolescent's developmental stage.	Child/adolescent's developmental stage is actively being assessed and taken into consideration for intervention planning.	Child/adolescent's developmental stage has been incorporated in the scope of intervention.	Child/adolescent's developmental stage is continually reassessed and reincorporated into intervention planning and execution.

FAMILY

Family Environmental Assessment Tool™
Domain Assessment Criteria

Enablers & Obstacles

Domain description:

Integration of the child/adolescent's primary environment(s) with current planning and approach to intervention:

- Physical environment, including access and safety.
- Tools, including technology and social media.
- Sensory considerations, including types and levels of stimulation.
- Impact of external routines and schedules.
- Range of settings and corresponding levels of exposure.

ENVIRONMENTAL

Domain goal: Environmental factors have been identified and are optimally assimilated into interventions.

Assessment Rating

Pre	Post
☐ Delayed	☐ Delayed
☐ Lagging	☐ Lagging
☐ In-progress	☐ In-progress
☐ On-task	☐ On-task
☐ Advanced	☐ Advanced

ASSESSMENT

Assessment Criteria

1	2	3	4	5
Delayed	Lagging	In-progress	On-task	Advanced
Aspects of the environment are negatively impacting the child's capacity for learning and growth.	Intervention planning and/or execution is occurring without incorporation of environmental elements.	Environmental elements are actively being investigated and taken into consideration for intervention planning.	Some environmental elements have been included in the scope of intervention.	Environmental elements are fully understood and assimilated into intervention planning and execution.

TOOL

Family Environmental Assessment Tool™
Domain Assessment Criteria

Support Systems

Domain description:

Family support systems inform current planning and approach to intervention:

- Community resources, including availability and access.
- Professional resources and networks.
- Family connections/friendships/neighborhood relationships.

Domain goal: Family has access to ample support systems in order to provide for their needs as they pertain to intervention.

Assessment Rating

Pre	Post
❒ Delayed	❒ Delayed
❒ Lagging	❒ Lagging
❒ In-progress	❒ In-progress
❒ On-task	❒ On-task
❒ Advanced	❒ Advanced

Assessment Criteria

1	2	3	4	5
Delayed	Lagging	In-progress	On-task	Advanced
Family does not have access to basic support systems.	Family may have access to some support systems, but they are is lacking in other basic support systems and/or not employing them.	All basic and/or desired support systems are either in place or are actively being investigated.	Family has all basic and/or desired support systems in place to enable productive intervention.	Family has all basic and/or desired support systems in place and is regularly employing them.

Child/Adolescent Readiness

Domain description:

Child/adolescent's inclination to adapt to experiences and engage with others based upon:

- Capacity for trust, curiosity, playfulness, perseverance and confidence.
- Response to environmental indicators of strengthened or weakened support.
- Emerging awareness of their knowledge base and attitudes toward learning.

Domain goal: Intervention is specifically tailored to the child/adolescent's unique disposition and readiness in a manner that promotes a desire for participation.

Assessment Rating

Pre	Post
☐ Delayed	☐ Delayed
☐ Lagging	☐ Lagging
☐ In-progress	☐ In-progress
☐ On-task	☐ On-task
☐ Advanced	☐ Advanced

Assessment Criteria

1	2	3	4	5
Delayed	Lagging	In-progress	On-task	Advanced
Intervention is performed in a manner that triggers a flight or fight response from child/adolescent.	Child/adolescent is not demonstrating a capacity to actively participate during interventions and is, therefore, limited to passive involvement.	Child/adolescent is demonstrating a capacity for at least partial involvement in interventions.	Child/adolescent is demonstrating a capacity for consistent participation in interventions.	Child/adolescent is actively seeking involvement in interventions and can assist in advancing the intervention trajectory.

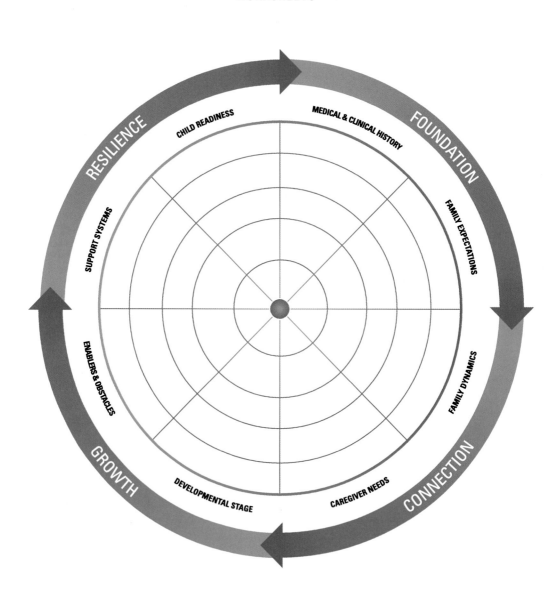

RESILIENCE

FOUNDATION

CONNECTION

GROWTH

CHILD READINESS

MEDICAL & CLINICAL HISTORY

FAMILY EXPECTATIONS

SUPPORT SYSTEMS

FAMILY DYNAMICS

ENABLERS & OBSTACLES

DEVELOPMENTAL STAGE

CAREGIVER NEEDS

WORKSHEETS

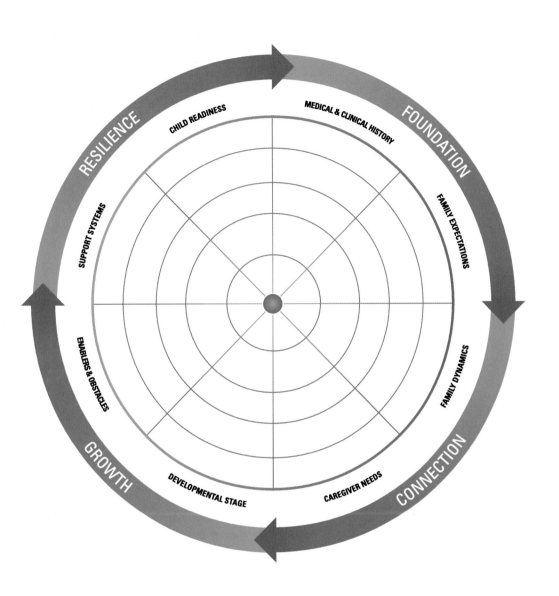

RESILIENCE

FOUNDATION

GROWTH

CONNECTION

CHILD READINESS

MEDICAL & CLINICAL HISTORY

FAMILY EXPECTATIONS

SUPPORT SYSTEMS

FAMILY DYNAMICS

ENABLERS & OBSTACLES

DEVELOPMENTAL STAGE

CAREGIVER NEEDS

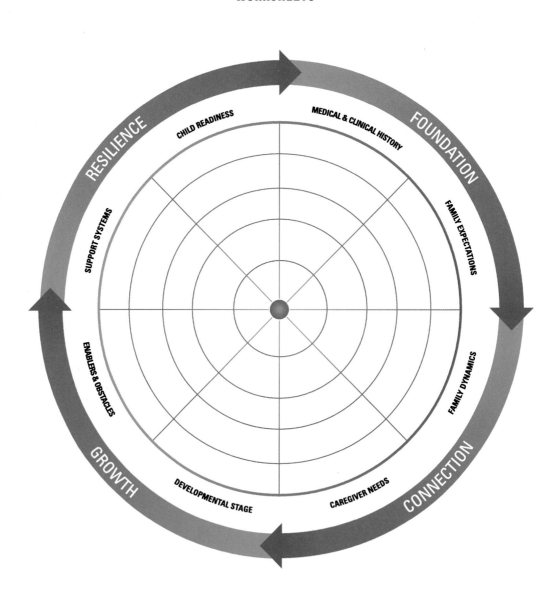

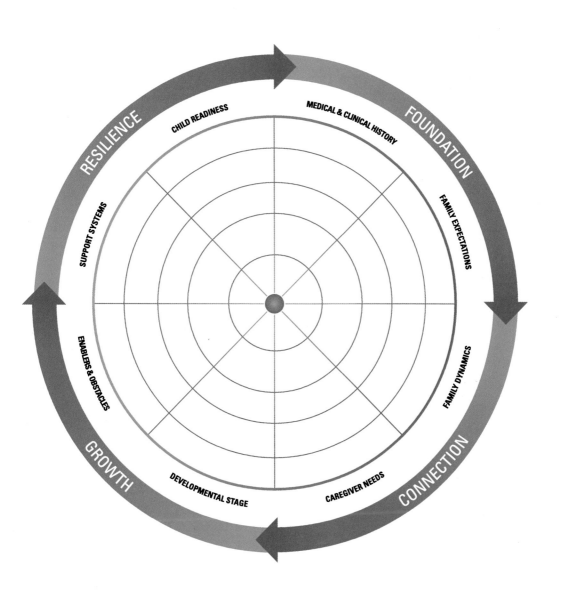

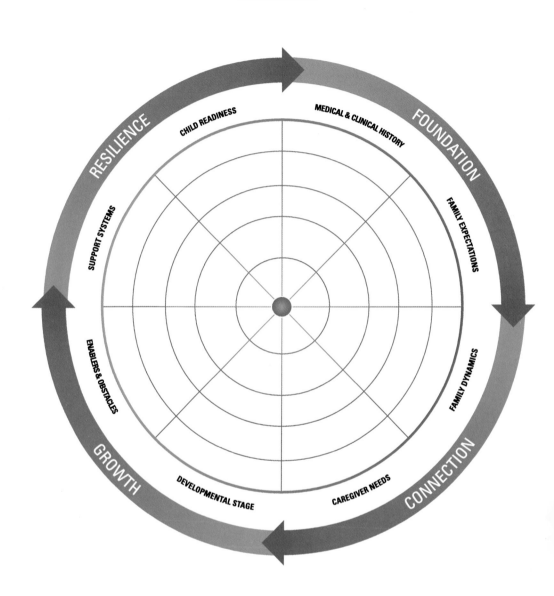

RESILIENCE

FOUNDATION

GROWTH

CONNECTION

CHILD READINESS

MEDICAL & CLINICAL HISTORY

FAMILY EXPECTATIONS

SUPPORT SYSTEMS

ENABLERS & OBSTACLES

FAMILY DYNAMICS

DEVELOPMENTAL STAGE

CAREGIVER NEEDS

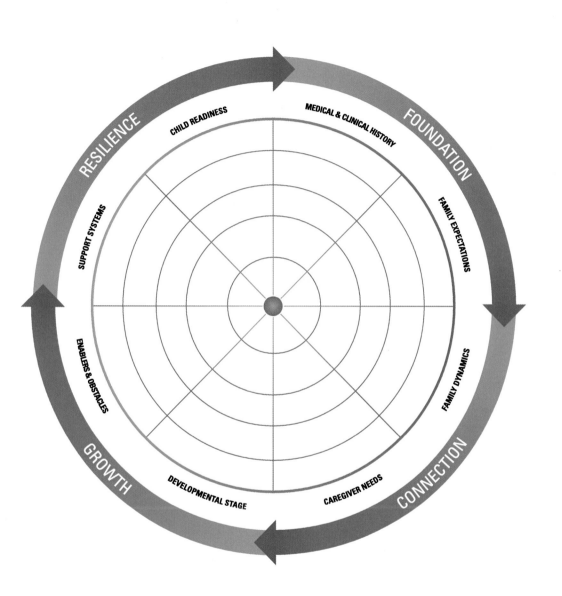

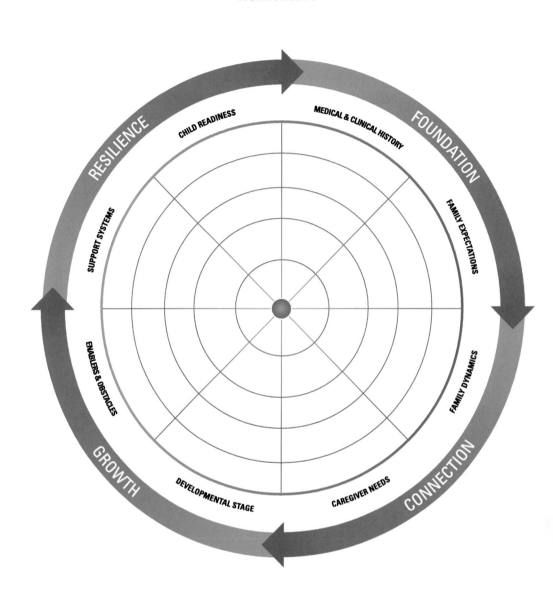

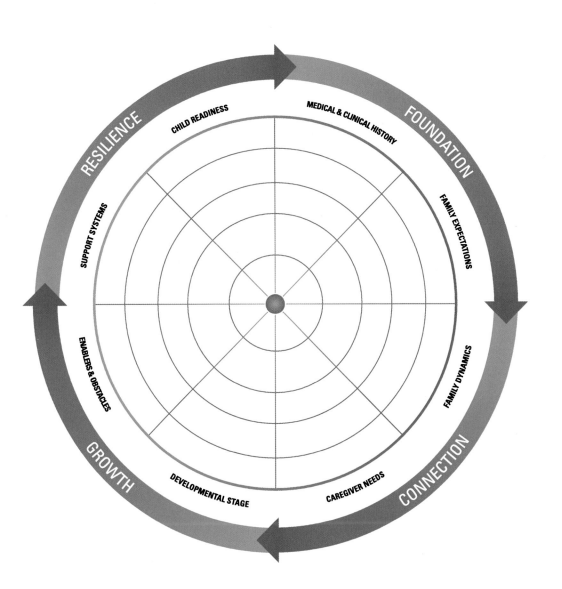

RESILIENCE

FOUNDATION

CONNECTION

GROWTH

CHILD READINESS

MEDICAL & CLINICAL HISTORY

FAMILY EXPECTATIONS

SUPPORT SYSTEMS

FAMILY DYNAMICS

ENABLERS & OBSTACLES

DEVELOPMENTAL STAGE

CAREGIVER NEEDS

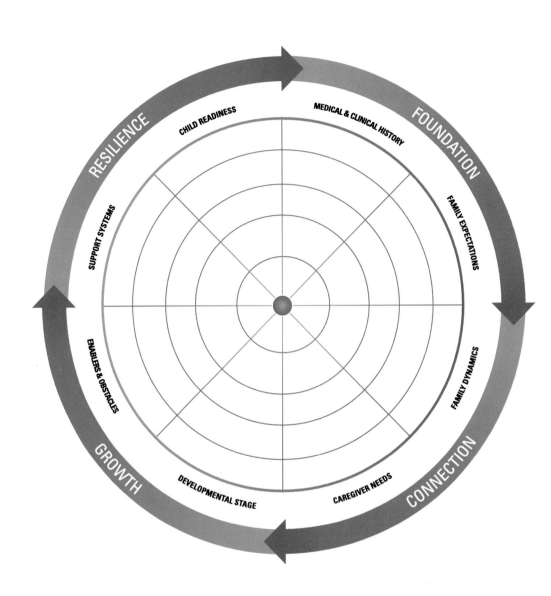

RESILIENCE

FOUNDATION

CHILD READINESS

MEDICAL & CLINICAL HISTORY

SUPPORT SYSTEMS

FAMILY EXPECTATIONS

ENABLERS & OBSTACLES

FAMILY DYNAMICS

GROWTH

CONNECTION

DEVELOPMENTAL STAGE

CAREGIVER NEEDS

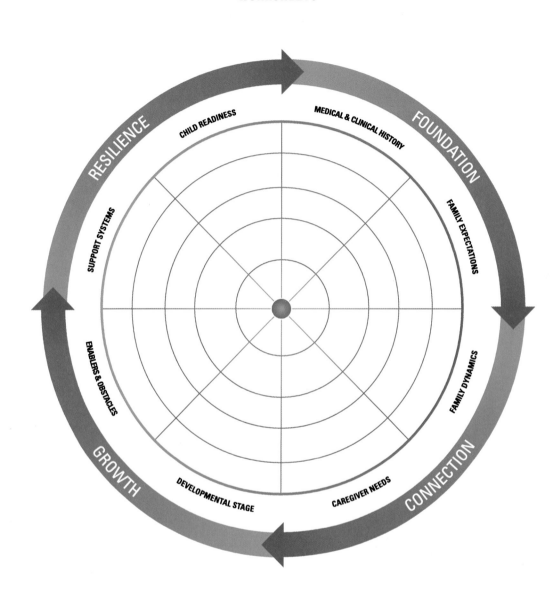

WORKSHEETS

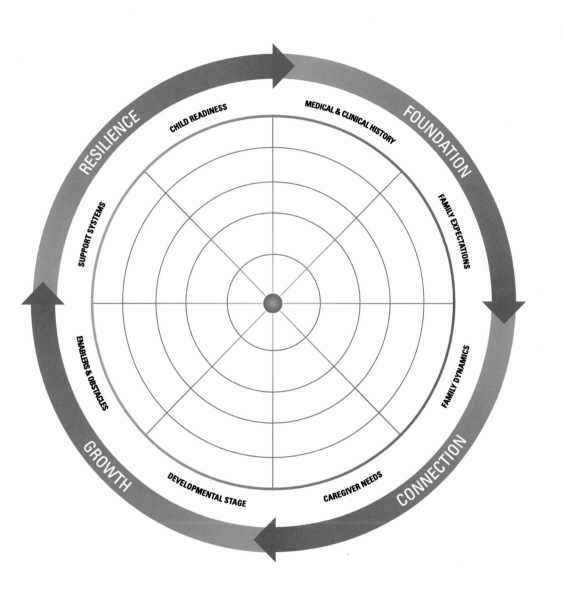

WORKSHEETS

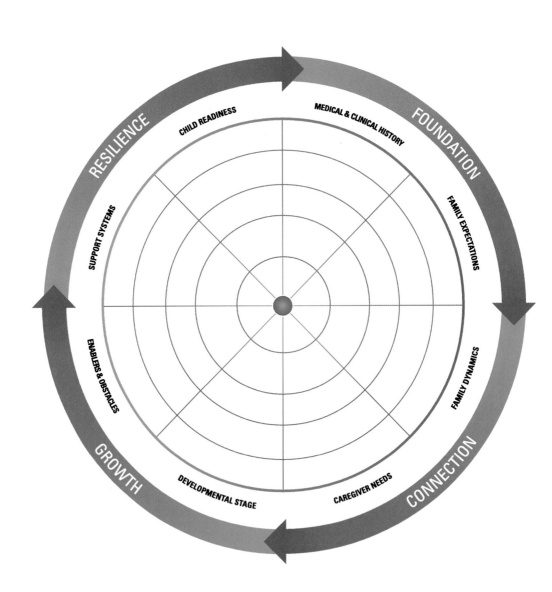

Labels on the wheel:

RESILIENCE

FOUNDATION

CONNECTION

GROWTH

CHILD READINESS

MEDICAL & CLINICAL HISTORY

FAMILY EXPECTATIONS

FAMILY DYNAMICS

CAREGIVER NEEDS

DEVELOPMENTAL STAGE

ENABLERS & OBSTACLES

SUPPORT SYSTEMS

WORKSHEETS

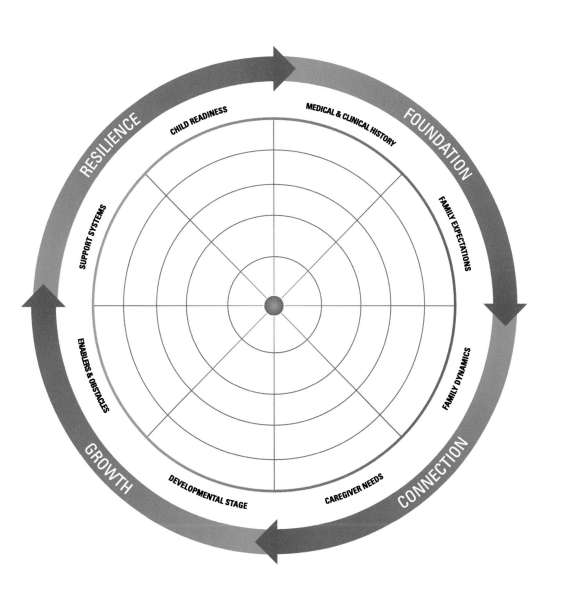

RESILIENCE

FOUNDATION

GROWTH

CONNECTION

CHILD READINESS

MEDICAL & CLINICAL HISTORY

SUPPORT SYSTEMS

FAMILY EXPECTATIONS

ENABLERS & OBSTACLES

FAMILY DYNAMICS

DEVELOPMENTAL STAGE

CAREGIVER NEEDS

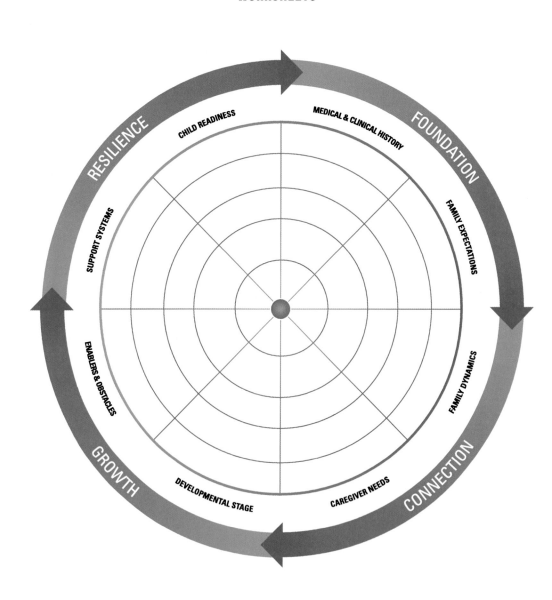

FOUNDATION

RESILIENCE

GROWTH

CONNECTION

CHILD READINESS

MEDICAL & CLINICAL HISTORY

SUPPORT SYSTEMS

FAMILY EXPECTATIONS

ENABLERS & OBSTACLES

FAMILY DYNAMICS

DEVELOPMENTAL STAGE

CAREGIVER NEEDS

WORKSHEETS

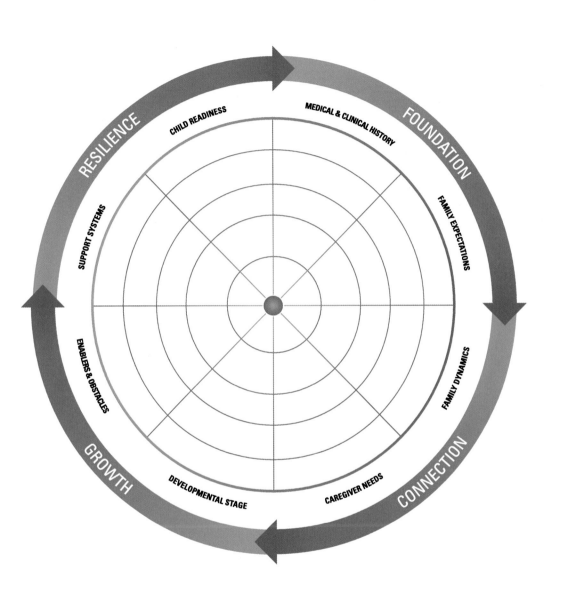

35

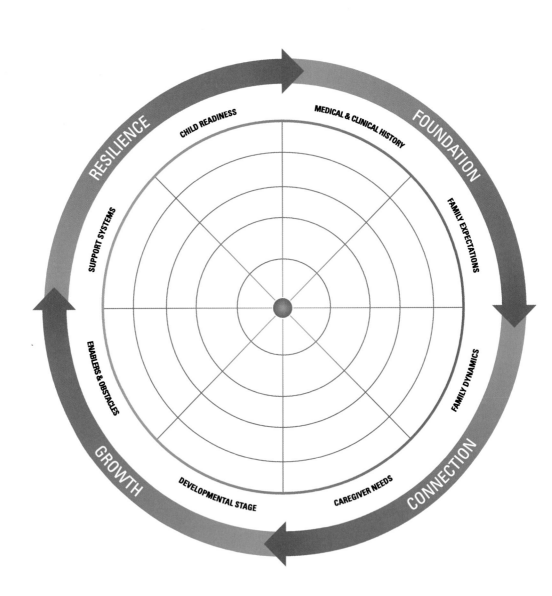

WORKSHEETS

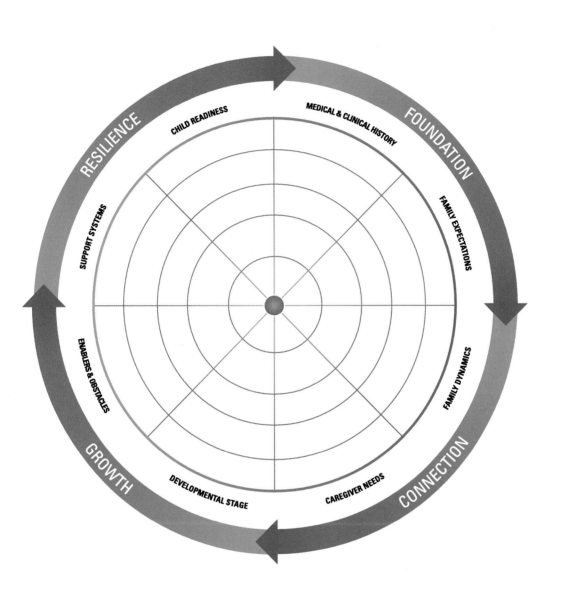

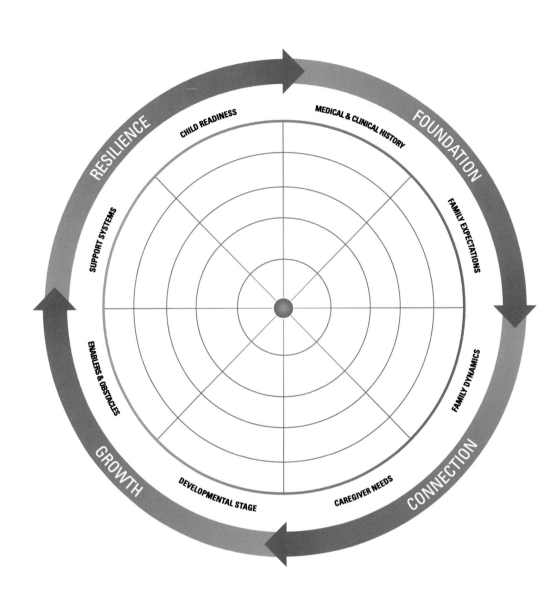

WORKSHEETS

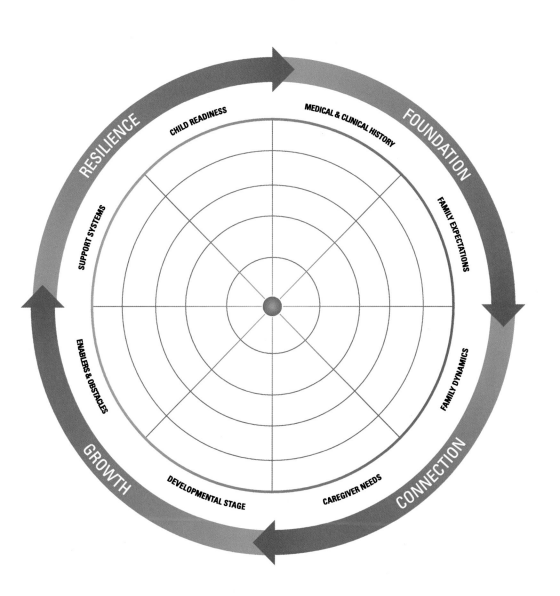

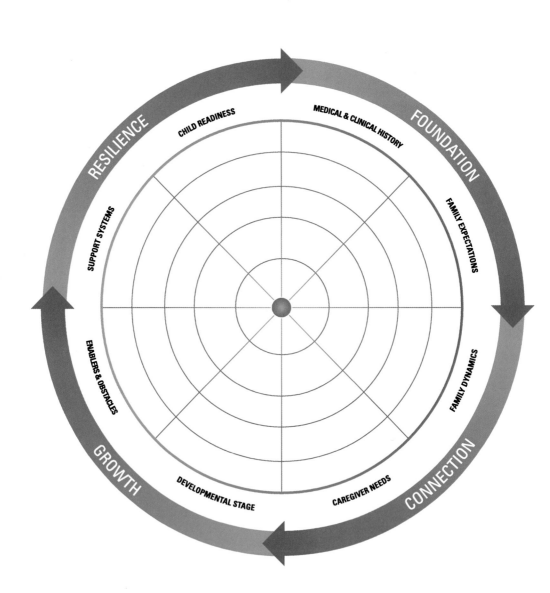

WORKSHEETS

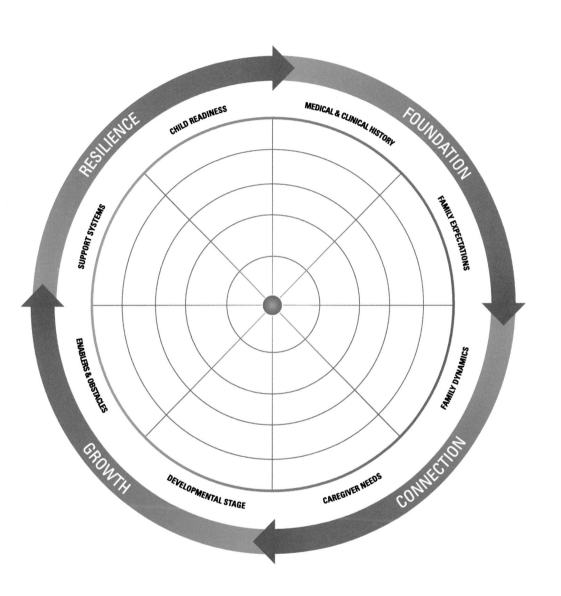

AUTHORS

Kerry Galarza, MS OTR/L is a pediatric occupational therapist and the Clinical Director of the Midwest Institute & Center for Workplace Innovation. She provides specialized assessment and intervention with children of all ages and their families. Kerry engages clients with naturally occurring, meaningful home-based methods to empower autonomy and maximize functioning. While providing focused experience in sensory processing disorder and the autism spectrum, Kerry partners with the network of professionals collaborating in the targeted care of each child's circumstances. Kerry also provides family-centered occupational therapy services addressing a range of developmental delays in collaboration with the Illinois Early Intervention Program.

Earning her bachelor's degree in Environmental Sciences and a Master's degree in Occupational Therapy from the University of Illinois, along with extensive training and an Associate's degree in Psychology from the Chicago School of Professional Psychology, Kerry specializes in helping her clients navigate the impact of the environment on their ability to thrive holistically.

AUTHORS

Steve Ritter, LCSW is a Licensed Clinical Social Worker and the Executive Director of the Midwest Institute & Center for Workplace Innovation. He is on the faculty of the Center for Professional Excellence at Elmhurst University where he earned the President's Award for Excellence in Teaching. His unique blend of training in the worlds of human resources, organizational development and psychology inspired the creation of the Team Clock® methodology, an approach that harnesses relationship cycles to empower growth in teams.

Earning a Bachelor's degree in Psychology from DePauw University and a Master's degree in Clinical Social Work from Loyola University of Chicago, Steve has researched the principles behind effective teams for over three decades and is the acclaimed author of Amazon Top-50 Business Book *Team Clock: A Guide to Breakthrough Teams*; *Useful Pain: Why Your Relationships Need Struggle*; *The Interpersonal Assessment Action Workbook* and *The 4 Stages of a Team: How Teams Thrive and What to Do When They Don't*.